Reading Excellence: Word Attack & Rate Development Strategies

REWARDS®

3rd EDITION

SECONDARY

Rate Development for Fluency ▶ Multisyllabic Word Reading ▶ Academic Vocabulary

Student Book

Anita L. Archer, Ph.D.
Mary M. Gleason, Ph.D.
Vicky Vachon, Ph.D.

Assisted by
Johnathan King
Scott Ricker
Pat Pielaet

Cambium LEARNING® Group | Sopris LEARNING

Cover Images: *Girl on left.* ©iStockphoto.com/CEFutcher. *Boy in center.* iStockphoto.com/Mark Bowden. *Teacher.* ©iStockphoto.com/mumininan. *Girl on right.* ©iStockphoto.com/monkeybusinessimages. page 123: ©iStockphoto.com/Lya_Cattel; ©iStockphoto.com/WilleeCole; ©iStockphoto.com/ Sandra Gligorijevic. page 124: ©iStockphoto.com/YanLev; ©iStockphoto.com/Nicholas Measures; ©iStockphoto.com/AnaBGD. page 125: ©iStockphoto.com/technotr; ©iStockphoto.com/BartCo; ©iStockphoto.com/acilo. page 126: ©iStockphoto.com/Otmar Winterleitner; ©iStockphoto.com/murat sarica; ©iStockphoto.com/ Ozgür Donmaz. page 127: ©iStockphoto.com/nemeziya; ©iStockphoto.com/cbeauche; ©iStockphoto.com/JacobH. page 128: ©iStockphoto.com/skynesher; ©iStockphoto.com/chrisjo; ©iStockphoto.com/Csondy. page 129: ©iStockphoto.com/PacoRomero; ©iStockphoto.com/JaniceRichard.

Printed in the United States of America

Published and Distributed by

17855 Dallas Pkwy, Suite 400 • Dallas, Texas 75287
800.547.6747 • www.voyagersopris.com

Contents

Letter to Students from the *REWARDS* Authors

Dear Students,

Welcome to the *REWARDS* program. This program will teach you how to read long words having two to eight parts. As you proceed through the grades, more and more of the words contain many parts. These long words are particularly important because they often carry the meaning in content-area textbooks.

In addition to learning strategies for reading long words, you will also be building your reading rate, or fluency. As you know from your own experience, it is not only important to read words accurately, but quickly. As you become a more fluent reader, you will be able to complete your reading assignments more quickly and will find recreational reading more enjoyable.

Thousands of students have used this program in the past and found it to strengthen their reading skills. We hope that you achieve the same gains and experience ever-increasing confidence in your reading.

May you reap all the REWARDS of this program.

Anita Archer
Mary Gleason
Vicky Vachon

ACTIVITY A: **Oral Activity—Blending Word Parts Into Words**

ACTIVITY B: **Vowel Combinations**

ay	ai	au
(say)	(rain)	(sauce)

ACTIVITY C: **Vowel Conversions**

a	i
(sound - c<u>a</u>t)	(sound - s<u>i</u>t)
(name - l<u>a</u>bor)	(name - p<u>i</u>lot)

ACTIVITY D: **Reading Parts of Real Words**

1	frain	trast	cay	scrip
2	fa *	tain	happ	ca *
3	laun	vi *	mid	stract
4	dit	plaud	tri *	claim

ACTIVITY E: Underlining Vowels in Words

1	waistband	fraud	midday
2	pigtail	vault	pathway
3	waylay	launch	railway
4	midway	blackmail	maintain
5	applaud	layman	mainstay

ACTIVITY F: Oral Activity—Correcting Close Approximations Using Context

ACTIVITY G: Prefixes and Suffixes

(dis)agree	dis
(mis)print	mis
(ab)normal	ab
(ad)mit	ad

ACTIVITY H: Circling Prefixes and Suffixes

1	addict	audit	damp
2	distract	ad-lib	display
3	admit	misfit	backspin
4	mislay	misplay	distraught
5	mast	banish	disclaim
6	misprint	distill	digit
7	disband	abstract	mismatch

ACTIVITY I: Meanings of Prefixes and Suffixes

mis = *wrongly, wrong, not*
dis = *not, opposite of*

a (Line 3) someone who does **not fit** with the rest of the group; a person whose looks, ideas, or behavior are quite different from a certain group

_____

b (Line 5) to do the **opposite of claim**; to give up a claim

_____

c (Line 6) a word or phrase that was **printed wrongly**; a printing error

_____

ACTIVITY J: Spelling Dictation

1		3	
2		4	

ACTIVITY K: Academic Vocabulary

1 **distract**—If someone or something **distracts** you, they take your attention away from what you are doing.

2 **admit**—If you **admit** that something bad or embarrassing is true, you agree, often unwillingly, that it is true.

3 **distraught**—If you are **distraught**, you are so upset and worried that you cannot think clearly.

4 **abstract**—**Abstract** ideas and **abstract** pieces of art are based on general ideas rather than specific people or things.

ACTIVITY A: Oral Activity—Blending Word Parts Into Words

ACTIVITY B: Vowel Combinations

er	ir	ur	ar
(her)	(bird)	(turn)	(farm)

1	ay	au	er	ai
2	ur	ar	ir	au

ACTIVITY C: Vowel Conversions

o	a	i
(sound - h<u>o</u>t)		
(name - l<u>o</u>cate)		

ACTIVITY D: Reading Parts of Real Words

1	naut	gov	sert	to *
2	turb	spa *	cur	mand
3	fraid	haul	gar	ver
4	tro *	crat	pli *	plaint

ACTIVITY E: Underlining Vowels in Words

1	garland	govern	fingernail
2	birthday	verdict	autocrat *
3	overhaul *	whirlwind	vitamin *
4	birdsong	curtail	surcharge
5	auburn	vertigo *	astronaut *

ACTIVITY F: Oral Activity—Correcting Close Approximations Using Context

ACTIVITY G: Prefixes and Suffixes

(in)complete   in

(im)possible   im

(com)pare   com

Prefixes

1	in	com	ab	mis	dis	in
2	im	mis	ad	im	ab	com

ACTIVITY H: Circling Prefixes and Suffixes

1	complaint	obtain	indistinct
2	absurd	impair	discard
3	disarm	carbon	interplay
4	imprint	disturb	insert
5	attic	inlaid	administer
6	implant	command	commit
7	cotton	mislaid	disinherit

ACTIVITY I: Meanings of Prefixes and Suffixes

in = *in, into*
im = *in, into*
mis = *wrongly, wrong, not*

a   (Line 5) **laid into** the surface of something, such as a table or a box

_____

b   (Line 6) something that is **planted into** the body during surgery

_____

c   (Line 7) **laid** down in the **wrong** place; something is put somewhere where you can't find it for a while

_____

ACTIVITY J: Spelling Dictation

1		3	
2		4	

ACTIVITY K: Academic Vocabulary

1 **distinct**—If something is **distinct**, you can hear, see, or taste it clearly.

2 **absurd**—If you say that something is **absurd**, you are saying that it's ridiculous or that it doesn't make sense.

3 **discard**—If you **discard** something, you get rid of it because you no longer want it or need it.

4 **administers**—If someone **administers** something such as a country, business, or organization, he or she takes responsibility for organizing and supervising it.

Review

1 distract

2 admit

3 distraught

4 abstract

ACTIVITY A: **Oral Activity—Blending Word Parts Into Words**

ACTIVITY B: **Vowel Combinations**

a - e (make)	o - e (hope)	i - e (side)	e - e (Pete)	u - e (use)
1 er	ir	au	ai	a - e
2 ar	u - e	ay	i - e	au
3 e - e	ir	ai	o - e	u - e
4 ur	ay	a - e	au	i - e

ACTIVITY C: **Vowel Conversions**

u (sound - c<u>u</u>p) (name - h<u>u</u>man)	o	a	i

ACTIVITY D: **Reading Parts of Real Words**

1 tude	mi*	plete	mote
2 hol	mo*	scribe	clude
3 bine	grate	na*	cro*
4 pose	gram	pede	spond

ACTIVITY E: Underlining Vowels in Words

1	holiday	austere	backbone
2	sustain	subscribe	automate*
3	costume	migrate*	stampede
4	suburb	autumn	microscope* *
5	obsolete*	attitude	riverside

ACTIVITY F: Oral Activity—Correcting Close Approximations Using Context

ACTIVITY G: Prefixes and Suffixes

(be)long	be	(pre)pay	pre
(de)forest	de	(pro)claim	pro
(re)print	re	(con)tinue	con

Prefixes

1	pro	be	pre	ad	dis	mis
2	con	in	im	com	ab	de
3	re	com	dis	con	pro	pre

ACTIVITY H: Circling Prefixes and Suffixes

1	betray	readjust	promote
2	disaster	reclaim	misbehave
3	prison	conclude	defraud
4	prepay	impose	combine
5	consume	prescribe	confine
6	respond	daytime	preprogram
7	propose	preplan	incomplete

ACTIVITY I: Meanings of Prefixes and Suffixes

re = *again, back*
pre = *before*

a (Line 2) to **claim back**; to get something back, such as your wallet, luggage, or other property

_____

b (Line 4) to **pay before** you get something

_____

c (Line 7) to **plan before** an event happens; to think about what you need before you carry out the plan for an activity, such as a science experiment or a picnic

_____

ACTIVITY J: Spelling Dictation

1		3	
2		4	

ACTIVITY K: Academic Vocabulary

1   **betray**—If you **betray** someone who trusts you, you do something that hurts or disappoints that person.

2   **confine**—To **confine** someone or something to a particular place means to keep that person or thing from leaving or spreading beyond the place.

3   **respond**—When you **respond** to something that is done or said, you react to it by doing or saying something yourself.

4   **propose**—If you **propose** a plan or an idea, you suggest it.

Review

1   distinct

2   absurd

3   discard

4   administers

ACTIVITY A: Oral Activity—Blending Word Parts Into Words

ACTIVITY B: Vowel Combinations

oi (join)		oy (boy)		or (torn)	
ay	oy	ai	er	ar	or
au	oi	ur	i - e	oy	ai
ir	e - e	oy	o - e	u - e	au

Row numbers: 1, 2, 3

ACTIVITY C: Vowel Conversions

i	u	o	a

ACTIVITY D: Reading Parts of Real Words

1 moil	saunt	lert	bord
2 ploy	mur	stub	do*
3 ster	cott	port	scape
4 tor	stroy	vide	mu*

ACTIVITY E: Underlining Vowels in Words

1	turmoil	saunter	borderline
2	oyster	murmur	partnership
3	tornado * *	transport	landscape
4	topsoil	boycott	asteroid
5	sirloin	stubborn	corduroy

ACTIVITY F: Oral Activity—Correcting Close Approximations Using Context

ACTIVITY G: Prefixes and Suffixes

(per)mit	per
(un)fair	un
(a)fraid	a

Prefixes

1	pro	a	pre	com	re	un
2	in	ab	mis	con	pre	dis
3	be	com	a	de	ad	per
4	un	a	con	com	im	pre

Circling Prefixes and Suffixes

1	persist	unafraid	discomfort
2	unfit	provide	uncertain
3	record	umpire	undertake
4	predict	pertain	reconstruct
5	accuse	confirm	misconduct
6	invalid	portray	imperfect
7	alert	contrast	advertise

ACTIVITY I: **Meanings of Prefixes and Suffixes**

un = not, opposite of
in = not, opposite of
im = not, opposite of

a (Line 2) **not fit**; not healthy

_____

b (Line 6) **not valid**; not true or not acceptable, such as a driver's license that has expired

_____

c (Line 6) **not perfect**; having flaws, such as a solution to a problem when the solution is not helpful

_____

ACTIVITY J: Spelling Dictation

1	3
2	4

ACTIVITY K: Academic Vocabulary

1 **persist**—If you **persist** in doing something, you continue to do it, even though it is difficult or other people are against it.

2 **record**—If you **record** a piece of information or an event, you write it down, photograph it, or put it into a computer so that you or others can refer to it in the future.

3 **predict**—If you **predict** an event, you say ahead of time that it will happen.

4 **contrast**—If you **contrast** one thing with another, you show or tell about the differences between the two things.

Review

1 betray

2 confine

3 respond

4 propose

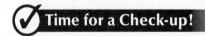 Time for a Check-up!

ACTIVITY A: Oral Activity—Blending Word Parts Into Words

ACTIVITY B: Vowel Combinations

ee (deep)	oa (boat)	ou (loud)

1	er	a - e	oy	o - e	ee	oi
2	au	ou	ai	oi	or	oa
3	e - e	ur	or	i - e	au	ir

ACTIVITY C: Vowel Conversions

e (sound - <u>le</u>t) (name - f<u>e</u>male)	a	u	i	o

ACTIVITY D: Reading Parts of Real Words

1	gree	rail	duce	fe *
2	vent	plore	ceed	treme
3	bound	teen	spect	board
4	coun	form	trode	aust

Underlining Vowels in Words

1	forlorn	evergreen	northwestern
2	referee	freedom	spellbound
3	canteen	cardboard	counterpart
4	monorail*	scapegoat	greenhouse
5	roadside	starboard	background

ACTIVITY F: **Oral Activity—Correcting Close Approximations Using Context**

ACTIVITY G: **Prefixes and Suffixes**

(ex)port	ex
(en)list	en

Prefixes

1	per	con	dis	a	pre	de
2	com	pro	en	ab	im	mis
3	ex	con	un	com	a	pre

ACTIVITY H: Circling Prefixes and Suffixes

1	protest	exclude	misinform
2	explore	prevent	encounter
3	return	engrave	reinstate
4	exceed	restart	unaware
5	regret	disagree	comprehend
6	extreme	employ	correspond
7	permit	destroy	reproduce

ACTIVITY I: Meanings of Prefixes and Suffixes

mis = *wrongly, wrong, not*
re = *again, back*

a (Line 1) to **inform wrongly**; to give the wrong information

_____

b (Line 3) to **turn back**; to go back to a place you have been before

_____

c (Line 4) to **start again**; to start something over again, such as an engine, your computer, or some aspect of your life

_____

ACTIVITY J: Spelling Dictation

1		3	
2		4	

ACTIVITY K: Academic Vocabulary

1 **exclude**—If you **exclude** someone from a place or activity, you prevent that person from entering the place or taking part in the activity.

2 **exceeds**—If something **exceeds** a particular amount, it is greater than, or more than, that amount.

3 **regret**—If you **regret** something that you have done, you wish that you had not done it, and, as a result, you feel sad or disappointed.

4 **comprehend**—If you cannot **comprehend** something, you cannot understand it.

Review

1 persist

2 record

3 predict

4 contrast

ACTIVITY A: Oral Activity—Blending Word Parts Into Words

ACTIVITY B: Vowel Combinations

ow
(low, down)

1	ou	ur	ar	oy	ow	oa
2	a - e	au	ai	ir	oi	ow
3	ar	or	ee	oy	ow	u - e

ACTIVITY C: Vowel Conversions

a	i	o	u	e

ACTIVITY D: Reading Parts of Real Words

1	ston	dow	gre*	trow
2	yond	slo*	larm	spair
3	laud	sper	flow	su*
4	thir	mag	shad	tern

ACTIVITY E: Underlining Vowels in Words

1	electrode	downhill	windowsill
2	outgrow	crossroad	overthrow *
3	elbow	downturn	showdown
4	trowel	flowerpot	fellowship
5	pillow	thirteenth	superpower *

ACTIVITY F: Oral Activity—Correcting Close Approximations Using Context

ACTIVITY G: Prefixes and Suffixes

book(s)	s		class(ic)	ic
runn(ing)	ing		van(ish)	ish
land(ed)	ed		art(ist)	ist
oper(ate)	ate		great(est)	est
use(less)	less		real(ism)	ism
kind(ness)	ness			

Prefixes

1	com	a	pre	con	mis	de
2	en	ex	per	dis	pro	be

Suffixes

3	ness	ish	ist	ate	ism	ic
4	less	ate	ish	est	ness	ist

ACTIVITY H: Circling Prefixes and Suffixes

1	softness	enthrone	hopelessness
2	specific	astonish	unfortunate
3	careless	energetic	magnetism
4	lowest	unselfish	powerlessness
5	vanish	alarmist	democratic
6	exhaust	deliberate	completeness
7	beyond	desperate	committee

ACTIVITY I: Meanings of Prefixes and Suffixes

ness indicates a *noun*
ness = *state of, condition of*

a   (Line 1) a **noun** that means the **state of** being **soft**

_____

b   (Line 1) a **noun** that means the **condition of** feeling **hopeless**;
     you are feeling so sad that you give up hope

_____

c   (Line 6) a **noun** that means the **condition of** being **complete**;
     having all the parts that something needs, such as a robot or
     a motorcycle having all of its parts

_____

ACTIVITY J: Spelling Dictation

1		**3**	
2		**4**	

ACTIVITY K: Academic Vocabulary

1 **astonishes**—If someone or something **astonishes** you, they surprise you very much.

2 **energetic**—An **energetic** person has a lot of energy. **Energetic** activities require a lot of energy.

3 **deliberate**—If something you do is **deliberate**, you decide ahead of time to do it.

4 **desperate**—If you are **desperate**, you are in a difficult situation and have little hope.

Review

1 exclude

2 exceeds

3 regret

4 comprehend

Lesson 7

ACTIVITY A: **Oral Activity—Blending Word Parts Into Words**

ACTIVITY B: **Vowel Combinations**

ow
(low, down)

1	oy	ow	ee	oa	ou	oi
2	au	ai	ar	ay	i - e	ow
3	a - e	ir	ow	oy	o - e	ur

ACTIVITY C: **Vowel Conversions**

i	e	u	a	o

ACTIVITY D: **Reading Parts of Real Words**

1	seem	show	gret	cau
2	gard	norm	da *	low
3	floun	crowd	marsh	stron
4	sham	clu *	trib	spec

ACTIVITY E: Underlining Vowels in Words

1	flounder	snowflake	powerhouse
2	shadow	download	overcrowd *
3	township	cauliflower	wheelbarrow
4	showcase	throwback	marshmallow
5	crossbow	shipwreck	outgrowth

ACTIVITY F: Oral Activity—Correcting Close Approximations Using Context

ACTIVITY G: Prefixes and Suffixes

care(ful) ful	farm(er) er
person(al) al	invent(or) or

Prefixes

1	a	com	con	dis	pre	re
2	im	ex	un	per	pro	a

Suffixes

3	est	ic	ful	or	al	er
4	ish	ism	less	ate	ness	ist

Circling Prefixes and Suffixes

1	personal	spectator	exaggerate
2	discover	optimism	disrespectful
3	careful	abnormal	uneventful
4	diminish	dramatic	redistribute
5	regretful	inspector	astronomer
6	abolish	gratitude	ungrateful
7	proposal	strongest	investigator

ACTIVITY I: **Meanings of Prefixes and Suffixes**

*ful indicates an **adjective***	*or or er indicates a **noun***
***ful** = full of*	***or** or **er** = person connected with*

a   (Line 3) an **adjective** that means **full of care**; you take a lot of care with what you are doing

_____

b   (Line 5) a **noun** that means a **person connected with astronomy**; a scientist who studies things in the sky, such as stars, planets, and asteroids

_____

c   (Line 7) a **noun** that means a **person connected with investigating**; someone who studies the details of a situation, such as a crime scene or a mysterious disease

_____

ACTIVITY J: Spelling Dictation

1		3	
2		4	

ACTIVITY K: Academic Vocabulary

1 **personal**—A **personal** opinion, quality, or thing belongs or relates to a particular person.

2 **exaggerates**—If someone **exaggerates**, he or she indicates that something is bigger, worse, or more important than it really is.

3 **abnormal**—Something that is **abnormal** is unusual, often in a way that is troublesome.

4 **abolish**—If someone in authority **abolishes** a practice, he or she puts an end to that practice.

Review

1 astonishes

2 energetic

3 deliberate

4 desperate

Lesson 8

ACTIVITY A: Oral Activity—Blending Word Parts Into Words

ACTIVITY B: Vowel Combinations

oo
(moon, book)

1	oa	oo	oi	ow	oy	ee
2	ou	er	ir	au	oo	ay
3	a - e	ur	ai	oo	ar	ow

ACTIVITY C: Vowel Conversions

e	u	i	o	a

ACTIVITY D: Reading Parts of Real Words

1	grad	wood	mort	hist
2	temp	cen	jur	pool
3	tre*	roof	glow	fault
4	drift	plain	flu*	look

ACTIVITY E: Underlining Vowels in Words

1	monsoon	loophole	boomerang
2	redwood	shampoo	footprint
3	lagoon	bookshelf	toothpaste
4	rooftop	textbook	overlook *
5	fireproof	hoodlum	driftwood

ACTIVITY F: Oral Activity—Correcting Close Approximations Using Context

ACTIVITY G: Prefixes and Suffixes

opin(ion)	ion	atten(tive)	tive
ac(tion)	tion	expen(sive)	sive
exten(sion)	sion		

Prefixes

1	com	a	ad	com	pre	ex
2	en	im	pro	in	ab	mis

Suffixes

3	ism	ist	ic	ion	tive	sion
4	tion	ful	al	sive	or	ate
5	or	est	sion	less	ion	al

ACTIVITY H: Circling Prefixes and Suffixes

1	billion	intentional	explanation
2	extensive	possession	perspective
3	opinion	precaution	recommendation
4	disorder	delightful	educational
5	disloyal	regardless	complication
6	external	exhaustive	comprehensive
7	adhesion	distasteful	provisional

ACTIVITY I: Meanings of Prefixes and Suffixes

pre = *before*
dis = *not, opposite of*

a (Line 3) a **caution** taken **before** doing something; something done ahead of time to prevent harm

_____

b (Line 4) the **opposite of order**; a state of messiness or confusion, such as a messy bedroom or a riot in the streets

_____

c (Line 5) **not loyal**; not being true to someone who trusts you

_____

ACTIVITY J: Spelling Dictation

1	3
2	4

ACTIVITY K: Academic Vocabulary

1 **intention**—An **intention** is an idea or plan of what you are going to do.

2 **explain**—If you **explain** something, you give details about it or describe it so that it can be understood.

3 **possess**—If you **possess** something, you have it or own it.

4 **external**—**External** means happening, coming from, or existing outside a place, person, or area.

Review

1 **personal**

2 **exaggerates**

3 **abnormal**

4 **abolish**

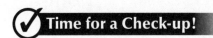 **Time for a Check-up!**

ACTIVITY A: Oral Activity—Blending Word Parts Into Words

ACTIVITY B: Vowel Combinations

oo
(moon, book)

1	ee	ow	oa	oo	ur	ai
2	oi	au	ar	oy	oo	or
3	u - e	oo	i - e	ay	er	ow

ACTIVITY C: Vowel Conversions

o	a	e	i	u

ACTIVITY D: Reading Parts of Real Words

1	foot	col	pone	stra *
2	south	blow	ber	whirl
3	sault	pend	vir	poon
4	tec	deem	hood	dent

1	bamboo	classroom	scrapbook
2	outlook	platoon	toothbrush
3	tattoo	firewood	midafternoon
4	maroon	barefoot	showroom
5	uproot	whirlpool	bridegroom

ACTIVITY F: **Oral Activity—Correcting Close Approximations Using Context**

ACTIVITY G: **Prefixes and Suffixes**

thirst(y)	y	mission(ary)	ary
safe(ly)	ly	odd(ity)	ity

Prefixes

1	be	com	en	a	ab	re
2	con	ad	im	dis	per	pre

Suffixes

3	er	ary	or	y	tive	ism
4	ion	ity	ly	sion	ary	ness
5	ic	sive	or	al	ful	est

ACTIVITY H: Circling Prefixes and Suffixes

1	absurdity	protection	contemporary
2	injury	profoundly	individuality
3	situation	collective	contaminate
4	history	conclusion	perfectionist
5	incentive	gradually	personality
6	seemingly	completion	immortality
7	capacity	expedition	precautionary

ACTIVITY I: Meanings of Prefixes and Suffixes

ion, *tion*, or *sion* *indicates a* **noun**
ion, *tion*, or *sion* = *act of, result of, state of*

a (Line 1) a **noun** that means the **act of protecting**; a person, place, or thing that keeps someone or something free from harm

_____

b (Line 4) a **noun** that means the **result of concluding**; a final decision about what is true after you have thought about all the information

_____

c (Line 6) a **noun** that means the **act of completing**; the act of having finished something, such as a year in school or an assignment

_____

ACTIVITY J: Spelling Dictation

1		**3**	
2		**4**	

ACTIVITY K: Academic Vocabulary

1 **contaminated**—If something becomes **contaminated** by dirt, chemicals, or radiation, it becomes impure or harmful.

2 **incentive**—An **incentive** is something that encourages you to do something.

3 **immortal**—Someone or something that is **immortal** is famous and likely to be remembered for a long time.

4 **expedition**—An **expedition** is an organized journey made for a particular purpose, such as exploration.

Review

1 intention

2 explain

3 possess

4 external

ACTIVITY A: **Oral Activity—Blending Word Parts Into Words**

ACTIVITY B: **Vowel Combinations**

ea
(meat, thread)

1	ou	ow	ea	oa	oi	ee
2	ai	au	ir	or	a - e	oo
3	ea	oy	ur	oo	or	ay
4	u - e	or	ow	ar	ea	er

ACTIVITY C: **Vowel Conversions**

u	o	a	e	i

ACTIVITY D: **Reading Parts of Real Words**

1	head	thor	stan	pow
2	moun	prac	vant	ped
3	stren	coast	proof	stead
4	ple*	mean	mize	poss

ACTIVITY E: Underlining Vowels in Words

1	teammate	steadfast	widespread
2	seaboard	farmstead	northeastern
3	meadow	peacetime	readership
4	deadlock	spearhead	downstream
5	headlong	meanwhile	mainstream

ACTIVITY F: Oral Activity—Correcting Close Approximations Using Context

ACTIVITY G: Prefixes and Suffixes

inform(ant)	ant	disturb(ance)	ance
consist(ent)	ent	occurr(ence)	ence
argu(ment)	ment		

Prefixes

1	ab	con	a	com	en	pro
2	ex	pre	per	un	mis	ad

Suffixes

3	tive	ant	ence	ent	ance	ly
4	ity	ment	y	ion	est	ary
5	ful	sive	sion	or	ant	al

ACTIVITY H: Circling Prefixes and Suffixes

1	influence	importance	postponement
2	rebellion	inexpensive	disinfectant
3	immediate	dependent	inconveniently
4	continent	informality	preliminary
5	endurance	exuberant	entertainment
6	difficulty	incidentally	determination
7	experience	inheritance	unemployment

ACTIVITY I: Meanings of Prefixes and Suffixes

ment indicates a noun
ment = act of, result of, state of

a (Line 1) a **noun** that means the **result of postponing**; a delay of something until later

b (Line 5) a **noun** that means the **act of entertaining**; the show or the play that entertains or amuses you

c (Line 7) a **noun** that means the **state of** being **unemployed**; the state of being without a job

Spelling Dictation

1		**3**	
2		**4**	

ACTIVITY K: Academic Vocabulary

1 **influence**—When people or things **influence** a person or situation, they have an effect on that person's behavior or that situation.

2 **dependent**—To be **dependent** on something or someone means to need that thing or person in order to succeed or survive.

3 **exuberant**—If you are **exuberant**, you are full of energy, excitement, and cheerfulness.

4 **determination**—**Determination** is the act of not letting anything stop you.

Review

1 contaminated

2 incentive

3 immortal

4 expedition

Lesson 11

ACTIVITY A: Oral Activity—Blending Word Parts Into Words

ACTIVITY B: Vowel Combinations

ea
(meat, thread)

1	au	oo	ow	ee	er	ai
2	ay	au	e - e	oy	ea	ur
3	oa	i - e	ir	ea	ar	oi
4	oy	ou	ea	oi	oo	au

ACTIVITY C: Vowel Conversions

a	i	u	o	e

ACTIVITY D: Reading Parts of Real Words

1	flex	serv	feath	mend
2	mar	bread	ize	muse
3	struc	weed	gla*	stream
4	ro*	line	stone	dund

ACTIVITY E: Underlining Vowels in Words

1	seaweed	headboard	southeastern
2	health	macaroon	leadership
3	headset	letterhead	streamline
4	daydream	meantime	bloodstream
5	deadline	pillowcase	gingerbread

ACTIVITY F: Oral Activity—Correcting Close Approximations Using Context

ACTIVITY G: Prefixes and Suffixes

nerv(ous)	ous	spe(cial)	cial
pre(cious)	cious	par(tial)	tial
cau(tious)	tious		

Prefixes

1	im	a	com	con	en	mis
2	con	per	en	ab	a	pre

Suffixes

3	ary	tial	tious	ance	al	ion
4	ance	ment	ent	ly	ity	ous
5	ant	cial	cious	tion	sive	tive

ACTIVITY H: Circling Prefixes and Suffixes

1 judicial	marvelous	pretentious
2 spacious	reconsider	substantial
3 strenuous	nutritious	documentary
4 delicious	influential	commercial
5 disappear	permanent	inconclusive
6 robbery	impractical	advertisement
7 gracious	continuous	independence

ACTIVITY I: Meanings of Prefixes and Suffixes

re = again, back
dis = not, opposite of
im = not, opposite of

a (Line 2) to **consider again**; to think again about something so you can decide whether to change it

_____

b (Line 5) to do the **opposite of appear**; to become invisible or go out of your sight

_____

c (Line 6) **not practical**; not good at practical matters, such as buying comfortable shoes for less money instead of fancy shoes for more money

_____

ACTIVITY J: Spelling Dictation

1		3	
2		4	

ACTIVITY K: Academic Vocabulary

1. **substantial—Substantial** means large in amount or degree.

2. **strenuous—A strenuous** activity or action involves a lot of energy or effort.

3. **permanent—Permanent** means lasting forever or occurring all the time.

4. **gracious—**If someone is **gracious**, he or she is polite and considerate.

Review

1. influence

2. dependent

3. exuberant

4. determination

ACTIVITY A: Oral Activity—Blending Word Parts Into Words

ACTIVITY B: Vowel Combinations

ea
(meat, thread)

1	ou	ea	oi	oo	er	ay
2	oy	au	i - e	ir	oa	ea
3	u - e	or	ou	ee	oo	ai
4	ur	ar	ow	ea	au	o - e

ACTIVITY C: Vowel Conversions

e	o	i	a	u

ACTIVITY D: Reading Parts of Real Words

1	rep	thread	fudd	deal
2	pun	vest	pell	stru *
3	furn	gleam	ti *	murd
4	glam	rupt	vate	ket

ACTIVITY E: Underlining Vowels in Words

1	benefit	authorize	marketplace
2	lifetime	coastline	dealership
3	solitude	torpedo ∗ ∗	cornerstone
4	domain ∗	schoolboy	mountainside
5	earshot	maximize	threadbare

ACTIVITY F: Oral Activity—Correcting Close Approximations Using Context

ACTIVITY G: Prefixes and Suffixes

cour(age)   age   agree(able)   able

pic(ture)   ture   revers(ible)   ible

                          tack(le)   le

Prefixes

1	per	a	con	com	ex	ad
2	pro	un	ex	im	dis	pre

Suffixes

3	ent	age	ture	cious	tial	le
4	ment	ion	ible	y	ance	able
5	ity	ary	ence	ant	ment	ous

ACTIVITY H: Circling Prefixes and Suffixes

1	legendary	unobservant	disadvantage
2	struggle	immature	uncomfortable
3	manage	impossible	revolutionary
4	feature	intolerant	misrepresentation
5	incapable	tremendous	incombustible
6	indecisive	competitive	perseverance
7	inflexible	disposable	unconventionality

ACTIVITY I: Meanings of Prefixes and Suffixes

un = *not, opposite of*
im = *not, opposite of*
in = *not, opposite of*

a   (Line 1) **not observant**; not seeing or noticing things around you

_____

b   (Line 2) **not mature**; childish

_____

c   (Line 4) **not tolerant**; not willing to accept people or ideas different from your own

_____

ACTIVITY J: Spelling Dictation

1		3	
2		4	

ACTIVITY K: Academic Vocabulary

1 **legendary**—If you describe something or someone as **legendary**, you mean that they are very famous and that many stories are told about them.

2 **feature**—A **feature** of something is an interesting, important, or distinct part or characteristic of it.

3 **capable**—If you are **capable** of doing something, you are able to do it.

4 **persevere**—When you **persevere**, you keep on trying to do something even if it is hard.

Review

1 substantial

2 strenuous

3 permanent

4 gracious

 Time for a Check-up!

ACTIVITY A: Vowel Combinations Review

1 oa   ay   oo   ee   a - e   er

2 or   oy   ir   i - e   ar   ou

3 au   oi   ai   e - e   ur   ow

ACTIVITY B: Vowel Conversions Review

i   e   a   o   u

ACTIVITY C: Prefixes and Suffixes Review

Prefixes

1 un   ab   dis   com   im

2 be   con   pro   a   en

Suffixes

3 age   able   sion   cial   ant

4 ence   al   ly   cious   ary

5 ity   sive   ous   ment   le

ACTIVITY D: Strategy Instruction

1 propeller   construction

2 infection   suddenness

3 befuddle   inartistic

4 exterminate   generosity

ACTIVITY E: Guided Strategy Practice

1 expansion   mobility

2 container   effective

3 performance   consultant

4 excellence   intensity

5 distinction   instruction

ACTIVITY F: Spelling Dictation

1	3
2	4

ACTIVITY G: Meanings of Prefixes and Suffixes

ity indicates a *noun*
ity = state of, quality of

a (Activity D) a **noun** that means the **quality of** being **generous**; the quality of wanting to share your time, money, or things with others

_____

b (Activity E) a **noun** that means the **quality of** being **mobile**; the quality of freely moving from place to place

_____

c (Activity E) a **noun** that means the **state of** being **intense**; the state of being extremely strong, difficult, or serious, such as color, light, physical activity, or emotions

_____

1 The dancer's performance was so artistic that I was sure I had never seen such excellence.

2 Although the propeller had been effective, it stopped with great suddenness.

3 The inspector checked the construction for perfection before we moved into the house.

4 Once the infection has spread, everyone needs instruction on how to get well.

5 Although scientists have learned a lot about hurricane prediction, they cannot predict the intensity of these storms.

6 Can you exterminate the ants before they consume all the food?

7 The expert told the basketball players how to befuddle the other team.

8 The container leaked; it was not effective for liquid matter.

9 An inartistic person completed that awful painting!

10 Seemingly, the new construction will result in expansion of the school.

*11 The food <u>consultant</u> helped the students plan a delicious dinner.

*12 The city awarded a medal of <u>distinction</u>, or excellence, to the police department for marvelous crime prevention.

List 1

1 caribou   *n.*   **Caribou** are members of the deer family, related to reindeer and elk.

2 Porcupine   *n.*   **Porcupine caribou** were named after the
        caribou   Porcupine River.

3 ecosystem   *n.*   An **ecosystem** includes all the plants and animals that live in a certain area along with the relationships they have with each other and with their environment.

* **4** organisms   *n.*   **Organisms** are plants or animals, including ones so small you cannot see them without using a microscope.

5 endangered   *n.*   An **endangered species** is a species, or
        species   specific kind of animal or plant, that may die out.

6 lichen   *n.*   A **lichen** is a simple plant that forms a branching or crust-like growth on rocks, tree trunks, or walls.

* **7** resources   *n.*   **Resources** are things such as land, minerals, plants, and animals that people have available to them and can use to meet their needs.

List 2

1 century   *n.*   A **century** is 100 years.

2 migrate   *v.*   When birds, fish, or animals **migrate**, they move from one place to another, usually during a particular season, to find a place for breeding or to find food.

3 populate   *v.*   If people or animals **populate** an area, those people or animals live there, often in large numbers.

4 survive   *v.*   If you **survive** in difficult circumstances, you manage to live or continue in spite of those circumstances.

5 predator   *n.*   A **predator** is an animal that kills and eats other animals (its prey).

* 6 balance   *n.*   A **balance** is a situation in which all the parts are equal in strength or importance.

* 7 appear   *v.*   If someone or something **appears**, they become visible or come into your sight.

ACTIVITY J: **Passage Reading and Comprehension**

Ecosystems and Porcupine Caribou

13	Each member of an ecosystem has a part to play. In a stable ecosystem, predators and prey must stay in balance. For example,
23	when snakes eat mice, the snakes help keep the numbers of mice in
36	check. On the other hand, if the snakes eat too many mice, it will
50	affect all of the animals that depend on mice for food. **(#1)**
61	All organisms must get their needs met so they can survive. For each
74	species in an ecosystem, survival of the population depends on food,
85	shelter, and safety. If the members of a species don't find enough to eat,
99	the number of animals decreases. If predators kill too many animals in
111	the species, the number also decreases. A species that decreases too
122	much could become an endangered species. These are likely problems
132	for any ecosystem. Let's look at caribou as an example. **(#2)**
142	Caribou are larger than deer but smaller than elk. Even though
153	caribou belong to the deer family, both males and females have
164	antlers. Many types of caribou live in the Arctic. The Porcupine
175	caribou herd lives near the Porcupine River, which is how they got
187	their name. The river runs through the northwestern part of Canada
198	and the northeastern part of Alaska. When the Porcupine caribou
208	migrate, many thousands of caribou move back and forth between the
219	mountains in Canada and the coastal plains in Alaska. They cross the
231	Porcupine River. **(#3)**
233	Porcupine caribou mainly eat plants called *lichen*, which they
242	find by digging holes in the snow. When the snow is too deep in the
257	mountains, it is difficult for them to find lichen and other plants. The
270	deep snow, as well as their hunger, spurs them to move in order to
284	survive. Being able to find food is critical. So, in the spring, the caribou
298	come down from the mountains and travel north to the coastal plains
310	to find food and have their calves. They head for a specific calving
323	area on the northern coast of Alaska. In this area, the snow tends to
337	melt the earliest and new plants appear soonest. There will be plenty
349	for the mothers and baby caribou to eat. **(#4)**
357	But, new caribou calves also means food for grizzly bears and other
369	predators that live in the mountains. Calves are easier to catch than
381	adult caribou. So the bears follow the Porcupine caribou to the calving
393	area and wait for the calves to be born. If the grizzlies kill too many
408	calves, it disturbs the ecosystem. **(#5)**

413	For centuries, a group of humans has also depended upon the
424	Porcupine caribou herd for survival. The group goes by the name
435	Gwich'in, which means *the people*. The Gwich'in are First Nation
445	members whose villages are situated along the Porcupine caribou's
454	migration route. The Gwich'in hunt the caribou as they go by. They
466	rely on the caribou's meat as a major source of food for the long,
480	cold, snowy winter. They also need the caribou as a resource for
492	making shelters, clothes, and tools. The Gwich'in, scientists, and
501	others are concerned that the Porcupine caribou's numbers are in
511	decline. If the caribou were to disappear, the Gwich'in would lose
522	their way of life. **(#6)**
526	

ACTIVITY K: Rate Development

Cold Timing [   ]   Practice 1 [   ]

Practice 2 [   ]   Hot Timing [   ]

ACTIVITY A: Vowel Combinations Review

1 au   ee   a - e   ou   i - e   ⬚oo⬚

2 er   or   oa   oy   ay   ur

3 ⬚ow⬚   oi   ai   ir   ⬚ea⬚   e - e

ACTIVITY B: Vowel Conversions Review

e   o   i   u   a

ACTIVITY C: Prefixes and Suffixes Review

Prefixes

1 en   con   re   un   pre

2 ad   ex   mis   de   a

Suffixes

3 er   ity   ism   ary   ible

4 ish   ture   tious   tion   ate

5 al   tive   ent   ance   le

ACTIVITY D: Strategy Instruction

1	adventure	community
2	indifferent	unmistakable
3	correction	fundamentally
4	consolidate	reinvestigate

ACTIVITY E: Guided Strategy Practice

1	defensive	destructive
2	desirable	disagreement
3	fantastic	informative
4	explosive	unreasonable
5	recapture	permission

ACTIVITY F: Spelling Dictation

1	3
2	4

ACTIVITY G: Meanings of Prefixes and Suffixes

> **un** = not, opposite of
> **dis** = not, opposite of
> **re** = again, back

a (Activity D) **not mistakable**; so obvious you can't make a mistake about it

_____

b (Activity E) the **act of not agreeing**; an argument about ideas or actions

_____

c (Activity E) to **capture back**; to get something or someone back, such as property or a prisoner

_____

ACTIVITY H: Word Reading Review

1	expansion	generosity
2	effective	befuddle
3	inartistic	exterminate
4	construction	excellence
5	distinction	performance

1   Although Jane enjoyed painting, she was quite inartistic.

2   The handbook for racecar drivers was informative and entertaining.

3   After the tornado destroyed many homes, the community displayed great generosity.

4   Maria looked to the movie's director for corrections in her performance.

5   Logan wanted permission to use his mother's car, but she was indifferent to his request.

6   The defensive backs on the football team were explosive.

7   It will be impossible to market this invention because it's not a desirable item.

8   The resourceful consultant helped the people plan for an adventure.

9   The investigator proclaimed concealment of his weapon.

10   Susan had to consolidate the leftover milk, so she poured the milk from all the small cartons into one larger container.

*11   The whole community felt great helplessness in the face of <u>adversity</u>; the destructive floods had washed away most of their homes.

*12   Josh polished his model car to perfection, making the convertible <u>sleek</u> and shiny.

ACTIVITY J: Content-Area Vocabulary

List 1

*1 scientific   *adj.*   The word **scientific** is used to describe things that relate to science.

2 element   *n.*   An **element** is something in the universe, such as oxygen, mercury, or gold, that is made up of one kind of atom.

3 atom   *n.*   An **atom** is the smallest piece of a certain element that still acts like that element.

4 molecule   *n.*   A **molecule** is formed when two or more atoms (alike or different) are joined together.

5 gallium   *n.*   The element **gallium** is a soft, silvery gray metal that melts easily when held in the palm of your hand.

6 surface   *n.*   The **surface** of something is its outer boundary.

*7 process   *n.*   A **process** is a series of actions that have a particular result, such as factory workers taking raw materials and changing them into something else.

List 2

1	matter	*n.*	**Matter** is the physical part of the universe, consisting mainly of solids, liquids, and gases.
2	energy	*n.*	**Energy** is power that provides heat or makes machines work; it comes from such sources as the food we eat, electricity, or the sun.
3	explode	*v.*	When something **explodes**, it suddenly releases its energy.
4	carbon dioxide	*n.*	In its natural state, **carbon dioxide** (CO_2) is a colorless, odorless gas that can be turned into a liquid or a solid under certain conditions.
5	vapor	*n.*	When the temperature of a liquid substance is increasing and the liquid substance is on its way to becoming a gas, it is called a **vapor** (e.g., water **vapor**, carbon dioxide **vapor**).
*6	alternatively	*adv.*	We use the word **alternatively** to talk about something different from what has just been said.
*7	approximate	*adj.*	If something is **approximate**, it is very close but not exactly the same as a certain number or a certain thing.

Passage Reading and Comprehension

What Causes Phase Changes?

14
27
38

On Earth, almost all matter is in a solid, liquid, or gas state. You've seen matter change from one state or phase to another. Think of ice melting or water boiling. Why do these phase changes happen? The scientific explanation involves energy and molecules.

44
57
67
79
90

All matter is made up of atoms. Most atoms join with other atoms to form molecules. The molecules in matter are constantly moving back and forth, even though you can't see the movement with your naked eye. Scientists say that the molecules are vibrating. You could say they are jumpy, like children who have trouble sitting still. **(#1)**

101
112
126
136
146
156

Molecules vibrate faster when any kind of energy is added to them, whether the energy is from the sun, from an oven, or from an explosion. Scientists define solids, liquids, and gases by how much their molecules vibrate. When enough energy is added, and the molecules become jumpier, a phase change occurs in which the matter changes from one state to another. **(#2)**

163
174
186
197
209
223
236
247
261
273

In a solid, the molecules vibrate slowly and are packed tightly together. When energy is added to a solid, the molecules get jumpier, they vibrate faster, and the space between them increases. If the molecules become too jumpy for a solid, the solid becomes liquid. This is what happens when you place an ice cube in the sunlight, and the solid ice becomes liquid water. This is also what happens if you play with a chunk of the element gallium, which melts at approximately 30°C. Put the gallium in the palm of your hand. Your hand heats up the solid gallium. The molecules in the gallium vibrate faster, and it becomes liquid. **(#3)**

275
285
295
308
319
333
345

Alternatively, when energy is lost, the molecules in matter slow down and the space between them decreases. For example, when energy is taken away from a liquid, the molecules slow down and move closer together, and the liquid becomes solid. This is what happens when you put liquid water into a freezer. It becomes a solid. This is also what happens when you pour the liquid gallium from your hand onto a cool countertop. It becomes solid again. **(#4)**

353	What happens when another element or a combination of two or
364	more different elements (a compound) goes through phase changes?
373	Consider the compound carbon dioxide. Just like other elements and
383	compounds, carbon dioxide can change from a gas to a liquid to a solid.
397	When carbon dioxide reaches the solid state, it is called "dry ice." It's
410	called that because it resembles ice, but it doesn't obviously act like
422	ice. To make dry ice, companies use an expensive process for turning
434	carbon dioxide gas into a liquid. Then they skim off the part that got
448	so cold it turned to "snow," and they make it into pellets or blocks.
462	Look for blocks of dry ice in a special freezer case in your grocery
476	store. But, be careful not to touch it! It will burn your hand. **(#5)**
489	Can you change the solid dry ice to a gas again? If your teacher
503	picked up a chunk of dry ice and put it into a bucket of water, you
519	would see bubbles rise to the surface and break. Fog would come out.
532	What you are seeing is carbon dioxide vapor on its way to becoming a
546	gas. You are seeing a phase change in action. Energy from the warmer
559	water is being added to the carbon dioxide molecules. The molecules
570	vibrate enough that the solid dry ice becomes a gas. **(#6)**
580	

ACTIVITY L: Rate Development

Cold Timing [   ]   Practice 1 [   ]

Practice 2 [   ]   Hot Timing [   ]

ACTIVITY A: Vowel Combinations Review

1	oy	oi	ea	oa	ee	a - e
2	oo	ur	ai	ow	i - e	o - e
3	oi	ow	au	ir	ea	e - e

ACTIVITY B: Vowel Conversions Review

a	e	i	o	u

ACTIVITY C: Prefixes and Suffixes Review

Prefixes

1	in	dis	per	im	re
2	con	un	ex	de	com

Suffixes

3	ful	sion	ly	ture	ant
4	tial	ible	le	ence	y
5	cial	al	ment	ary	able

ACTIVITY D: Strategy Instruction

1. exceptionally   discussion

2. amendment   indigestible

3. intermission   formulate

4. torrential   investigation

ACTIVITY E: Guided Strategy Practice

1. reflective   consistent

2. amusement   intolerable

3. potential   administrative

4. instructor   predictable

5. companion   unprofessional

ACTIVITY F: Spelling Dictation

1	3
2	4

ACTIVITY G: Meanings of Prefixes and Suffixes

> *able* or *ible* indicates an *adjective*
> *able* or *ible* = able to be

a (Activity D) an **adjective** that means **not able to be digested**; something cannot be broken down inside the body, such as bones, fur, or feathers that an owl swallows but cannot digest

_____

b (Activity E) an **adjective** that means **not able to be tolerated**; something is difficult to put up with, such as something unpleasant or painful

_____

c (Activity E) an **adjective** that means **able to be predicted**; you can tell ahead of time what will happen

_____

ACTIVITY H: Word Reading Review

1	effective	exterminate
2	consolidate	informative
3	indifferent	reinvestigate
4	adventure	generosity
5	destructive	fundamentally

1 The instructor led a discussion about magnets and magnetism.

2 His companion's sarcastic remarks were a source of amusement.

3 The timing of a thunderstorm is unpredictable, so spectators have to be ready to scramble for shelter.

4 After much disagreement and argument, Congress passed the amendment.

5 Julie is dependent on her companion for help in preparing meals.

6 Marco said the new administrative team had great potential.

7 At intermission, Trevor and Janis had an important discussion while waiting at the drinking fountain.

8 Many pop singers deliberately try to recapture the magic of their first recording.

9 With great determination, the inventor is going to reinvestigate his idea.

10 The company's logo had an unprofessional appearance; it was a disaster.

*11 The assistant coach must <u>formulate</u> a plan for the defensive team.

*12 When the <u>torrential</u> rainstorms finally stopped, the community began dealing with all the damage.

List 1

1 biome   *n.*   A **biome** is a group of plants and animals that live in a particular region because they are suited to that region's physical environment.

2 tundra   *n.*   The **tundra** is a biome consisting of large flat areas of land in the north of Europe, Asia, and North America. The ground below the top layer of soil is always frozen and no trees grow there.

3 taiga   *n.*   The **taiga** is a biome of thick forest in the far north of Europe, Asia, and North America, situated immediately south of the tundra.

4 temperate forest   *n.*   The **temperate forest** is a biome in the Northern and Southern Hemispheres that has four seasons and is home to many plant and animal species.

5 tropical rain forest   *n.*   The **tropical rain forest** is a biome near the Earth's equator that is warm and wet.

*6 characteristic   *n.*   A **characteristic** is a feature or quality that is typical of a person, place, or thing.

*7 properties   *n.*   **Properties** are the characteristics or qualities that are typical of a place, an object, or a group of objects.

List 2

1 climate   *n.*   The **climate** consists of the weather conditions that are typical of a certain region.

2 precipitation   *n.*   **Precipitation** can be rain, snow, or hail.

3 centimeter   *n.*   A **centimeter** is a unit of length in the metric system equal to ten millimeters or one hundredth of a meter.

4 annual   *adj.*   **Annual** quantities or rates are related to a period of one year.

5 organisms   *n.*   **Organisms** are plants or animals, including ones so small you cannot see them without using a microscope.

***6** abundant   *adj.*   Something that is **abundant** is present in large quantities.

***7** determine   *v.*   To **determine** a fact means to discover it as a result of investigation.

Land Biomes

14	Would you be surprised to see a polar bear living in a desert? Of course you would. You know that polar bears live in a different kind
27	of area. Scientists have determined that Earth can be divided into
38	eight different areas called biomes. A biome is a large ecosystem
49	with characteristic organisms and nonliving factors throughout. Each
57	biome has certain properties, such as the amount of sunlight, range of
69	temperature, and the amount of precipitation. (#1)
75	The tundra is a land biome with an annual precipitation of nearly
87	twenty centimeters and with mosses and plantlike organisms called
96	lichens. The temperature in the tundra ranges from -60°C in the winter
108	to 15°C in the summer.
113	Most precipitation in the tundra is in the form of snow, and
125	most of the ground is also frozen. During the short summer, the
137	soil thaws through just the top few centimeters. Deeper than that is
149	the permafrost, a layer of soil that is frozen all year. Because of the
163	permafrost, no plants with deep-reaching root systems can grow.
173	Trees can't grow in the tundra. (#2)
179	The taiga (TI guh) is a land biome with an annual precipitation of
190	nearly fifty centimeters. Conifers are the characteristic plants. They
199	are the main kind of tree. The temperature in the taiga ranges from
212	-35°C in the winter to 20°C in the summer.
221	Much of the precipitation is in the form of rain. There is also a lot
236	of fog. Because the temperature is above 0°C for a longer period of
249	time in the taiga than it is in the tundra, the soil thaws completely each
264	year. The soil, though, is very wet and acidic. The acid condition is
277	caused by peat mosses and conifers that grow in the taiga. (#3)
288	The temperate forest is a land biome with an annual precipitation
299	of one hundred centimeters. Deciduous trees are the characteristic
308	plants. The temperature in the temperate forest ranges from -30°C in
319	the winter to 40°C in the summer. The temperate forest biome has four
332	distinct seasons each year: spring, summer, autumn, and winter. (#4)
341	The tropical rain forest is a land biome with an annual precipitation
353	of nearly two hundred to four hundred centimeters of rainfall. Vines
364	and broadleaf trees are the characteristic plants. The temperature
373	in the tropical rain forest is nearly the same all year, around 25°C.
386	Rainfall is abundant all year in a tropical rain forest.

396	The growing season lasts all year long in the tropical rain forest.
408	Plants grow very well in the warm, wet climate. More kinds of plants
421	grow in this biome than in any other. **(#5)**
429	

ACTIVITY L: **Rate Development**

Cold Timing [＿＿＿＿]   **Practice 1** [＿＿＿＿]

Practice 2 [＿＿＿＿]   **Hot Timing** [＿＿＿＿]

ACTIVITY A: Vowel Combinations Review

1	a - e	ar	oy	oo	er	u - e
2	ir	ow	o - e	au	or	oi
3	oo	ai	ow	ea	ay	e - e

ACTIVITY B: Vowel Conversions Review

o	i	e	a	u

ACTIVITY C: Prefixes and Suffixes Review

Prefixes

1	ab	de	mis	in	com
2	con	ad	per	un	im

Suffixes

3	ness	ance	y	ate	or
4	ant	ment	ion	ary	age
5	tious	ist	le	est	tive

ACTIVITY D: Guided Strategy Practice

1	completely		immediately
2	tentatively		decompression
3	absorbent		discriminate
4	laminate		inflammable

ACTIVITY E: Unguided Strategy Practice

1	apartment		glamorously
2	impanel		refreshment
3	premature		dissatisfaction
4	reduction		astonishingly
5	distrustful		unmanageable

ACTIVITY F: Spelling Dictation

1		**3**	
2		**4**	

ACTIVITY G: Meanings of Prefixes and Suffixes

in = *in, into*
im = *in, into*
pre = *before*

a   (Activity D) **able to be** quickly **in flames**; could catch fire easily and burn rapidly, such as paper or gasoline

_____

b   (Activity E) to enroll **in a panel**; to choose people to serve, such as on a jury

_____

c   (Activity E) **before** it is **mature**; too early or not time yet, such as a baby born too early or naming the winner of an election before everyone has voted

_____

ACTIVITY H: Word Reading Review

1	instructor	investigation
2	amendment	unreasonable
3	informative	intermission
4	intolerable	unprofessional
5	potential	administrative

ACTIVITY I: Sentence Reading

1 The unmanageable work led to job dissatisfaction.

2 The instructor and his students stared at the room's futuristic appearance.

3 Decompression sickness is not as severe for an astronaut as for a diver.

4 We were completely thrown into turmoil by Jake's distrustful words.

5 The astonishingly high heat in the desert is almost intolerable and could be deadly.

6 It's against the law for an employer to discriminate unfairly against anyone.

7 Unfair and persistent discrimination is likely to be destructive.

8 After the other team won the game, the athletes of the opposing team immediately stepped forward to congratulate the winners.

9 Carlos and Rose were so tired and thirsty that they went immediately to the refreshment counter.

10 The apartment was decorated very glamorously.

*11 Suddenly, Mario was so <u>famished</u> that he grabbed the disposable containers full of leftovers.

*12 There was a <u>reduction</u> in the apartment's rent; they are paying less now.

List 1

1 Europe   *n.*   **Europe** is one of the world's seven continents.

2 United   *n.*   The **United Kingdom** is an island country
   Kingdom   in Europe.

3 Ireland   *n.*   **Ireland** is the name of an island that is
                          west of the larger island of the United
                          Kingdom.

4 Emerald Isle   *n.*   **Emerald Isle** is a name given to Ireland
                          because of its green countryside.

5 famine   *n.*   A **famine** is a situation in which large
                          numbers of people have little or no food,
                          and many of them die.

* 6 emigrate   *v.*   If you **emigrate**, you leave your own
                          country to live in another country.

* 7 official   *adj.* If something is **official**, the government
                          or someone in authority has approved it.

List 2

* **1**   develops   *v.*   When someone or something **develops**, they grow or change over a period of time and usually become more advanced, complete, or severe.

2   economy   *n.*   An **economy** is the system that a country or region uses to organize its money, industry, and commerce.

3   manufacture   *v.*   When you **manufacture** things, you make products from raw materials, by hand or with a machine.

4   export   *v.*   To **export** products or raw materials means to sell them to another country.

* **5**   contribute   *v.*   If you **contribute** to something, you say or do something to bring about a successful result.

6   uniform   *adj.*   If you describe a number of things as **uniform**, you mean that they are all the same.

7   ancestors   *n.*   **Ancestors** are people in our family who came before us, such as our grandparents and great-grandparents.

The Emerald Isle

14	If you could fly over Ireland on a summer day, you would see lush green meadows and tree-covered hills. Surrounded on three sides
24	by the Atlantic Ocean, Ireland's green color is so striking that it was
37	named the Emerald Isle. (#1)

The Landscape

41	**The Landscape**
43	At Ireland's center lies a wide, rolling plain dotted with low hills.
55	Forests and farmland cover this central lowland. Much of the area is
67	rich in peat, or wet ground with decaying plants that can be used for
81	fuel. Peat is dug from bogs, or swampy lands.
90	Along the Irish coast, the land rises in rocky highlands. In some
102	places, however, the central plain spreads all the way to the sea.
114	Dublin, Ireland's capital, is on an eastern stretch of the plain. (#2)

The Climate

125	**The Climate**
127	Whether plain or highland, no part of Ireland is more than 70 miles
140	from the sea. This nearness to the sea gives Ireland a uniform climate.
153	Like the United Kingdom, Ireland is warmed by moist winds blowing
164	over the North Atlantic Current. The mild weather, along with frequent
175	rain and mist, makes Ireland's landscape green year-round. (#3)

The Economy

184	**The Economy**
186	Ireland has few mineral resources. The country, however, does have
196	rich soil and pastureland. The mild and rainy climate favors farming.
207	In the mid-1800s, Irish farmers grew potatoes as their main food
219	crop. When too much rain and a blight caused the potatoes to rot in
233	the fields, famine struck, bringing hardship to the Irish. This disaster
244	forced many Irish to emigrate to other countries, especially to the
255	United States. (#4)
257	Although farming is still important to Ireland, industry now also
267	contributes to economic development. The economy depends on the
276	manufacturing of machinery and transportation equipment exported
283	to the United Kingdom and the European mainland. Ships bringing
293	mineral and energy resources to Ireland dock at the country's many
304	ports, including Dublin and Cork. (#5)

309	**The People**
311	Most of the Irish trace their ancestry to groups of people who
323	settled Ireland more than 7,000 years ago. The Celts and British made
335	the biggest impact. Their languages—Gaelic and English—are Ireland's
345	two official languages today. Most Irish, however, speak English as
355	their everyday language. **(#6)**
358	**Influences of the Past**
362	Stormy politics mark Ireland's history. From the 1100s to the early
373	1900s, the British governed Ireland. Religion and government controls
382	mixed to cause disagreement. The Irish people resisted British rule
392	and demands that the Roman Catholic country become Protestant.
401	British officials seized land in Ireland and gave it to English and
413	Scottish Protestants. At one time the British drove out Irish Catholics
424	to make room for the new settlers. **(#7)**
431	

ACTIVITY L: Rate Development

Cold Timing [ ]   **Practice 1** [ ]

Practice 2 [ ]   **Hot Timing** [ ]

ACTIVITY A: **Vowel Combinations Review**

1	ay	a - e	au	oo	o - e	er
2	ee	oi	ur	i - e	ai	ow
3	ir	oy	ou	or	ea	u - e

ACTIVITY B: **Vowel Conversions Review**

a	u	e	i	o

ACTIVITY C: **Prefixes and Suffixes Review**

Prefixes

1	a	pre	re	un	mis
2	pro	ab	con	com	per

Suffixes

3	ic	ful	ly	ary	less
4	tion	ous	ist	ance	able
5	le	sive	tial	age	ture

ACTIVITY D: Guided Strategy Practice

1	occupation	inventiveness
2	suspicious	indescribable
3	surprisingly	communication
4	commemorate	instrumentalist

ACTIVITY E: Unguided Strategy Practice

1	cautious	confidence
2	cultivate	organization
3	defendant	disconnect
4	demolish	incredible
5	culminate	unglamorous

ACTIVITY F: Spelling Dictation

1	3
2	4

ACTIVITY G: Meanings of Prefixes and Suffixes

> **ous, tious,** or **cious** indicates an **adjective**
> **ous, tious,** or **cious** = full of

a (Activity D) an **adjective** that means **full of suspicion**; giving the impression that someone or something has done something wrong

_____

b (Activity E) an **adjective** that means **full of caution**; very careful, usually in order to avoid danger

_____

c (Activity E) an **adjective** that means **not full of glamour**; no more interesting than ordinary people or things

_____

ACTIVITY H: Word Reading Review

1	completely	reduction
2	companion	intermission
3	discriminate	immediately
4	tentatively	unmanageable
5	investigation	dissatisfaction

Sentence Reading

1. Surprisingly, the refreshments were prepared and delivered just in time for the party.

2. Governments have created special stamps to commemorate the lives of scientists, inventors, explorers, and many others.

3. Many farmers intentionally cultivate grazing grass for their livestock.

4. Some people are unpredictable because their actions are inconsistent with their words.

5. Martina and Jared tentatively agreed to start the investigation after they finished their administrative tasks.

6. The fifteenth century development of the toothbrush continues to affect us; surprisingly, many teens name it as the invention they depend on the most.

7. Michael's inventiveness will culminate in a new sports car design.

8. As of 2012, only twelve people have walked on the Earth's moon and can tell us their perspective of the incredible experience.

9. The chimp's playfulness captivates even those people who appear to be indifferent.

10. Marty is an instrumentalist, not a singer.

11. Many schools have some sort of Internet connection, but evidence shows a need to modernize it; that is, to make it the best we can in the present day.

12. Ireland's Great Famine in the mid-1800s caused indescribable suffering.

List 1

1 Galileo Galilei   *n.*   **Galileo Galilei** (1564-1642) was an Italian scientist who improved the telescope and changed how scientists conduct science.

* **2** curious   *adj.*   When you are **curious**, you are eager to know or learn something.

3 revolves   *v.*   When something **revolves** around another object, it moves in orbit around that other object.

4 telescope   *n.*   A **telescope** is an instrument that makes distant things seem larger and nearer when you look through it.

* **5** hypothesis   *n.*   A **hypothesis** is an idea that is suggested as a possible explanation for a particular situation or condition, but which has not yet been proved to be correct.

6 measure   *v.*   When you **measure** something, you figure out the size or amount in such units as inches, centimeters, miles, or kilometers.

7 data   *n.*   You can refer to information as **data**, especially when it is in the form of facts or statistics that you can analyze.

List 2

1 investigate *v.* If someone **investigates** an event, situation, or claim, they try to find out what happened or what is the truth.

2 method *n.* A **method** is a particular way of doing something.

* 3 observe *v.* If you **observe** a person or thing, you watch them carefully, especially in order to learn something about them.

4 describe *v.* If you **describe** a person, object, event, or situation, you say what they are like or what happened.

* 5 evidence *n.* **Evidence** is anything that makes you believe something is true or has really happened.

6 document *v.* If you **document** something, you make a detailed record of it by writing it down, photographing it, or putting it into a computer.

7 transform *v.* To **transform** someone or something means to change them completely.

Galileo's Science

Galileo Galilei is one of the most famous scientists in history.
11 | Among middle school and high school students, he is probably best
22 | known for discoveries he made with his telescope. But scientists also
33 | talk about him as someone who described new ways to do science.
45 | Today, most people take for granted that science uses observations and
56 | measurements. But, until Galileo's time—the 17th century—scientists
65 | didn't always gather evidence to support their explanations. There
74 | were no clocks, thermometers, or telescopes for learning about nature.
84 | Those who explained the world to others used mainly logic. Galileo's
95 | inventions and methods transformed science. As you read about one of
106 | his investigations, notice the way he worked. **(#1)**

113 | One night, Galileo turned his telescope toward the brightest thing
123 | he could see from his window, Jupiter. Next to Jupiter he saw three
136 | "starlets" that were, in his words, "in an exact straight line parallel to
149 | the ecliptic." Galileo reported that the starlets stirred his curiosity. He
160 | wondered if the starlets were merely fixed stars that happened to be
172 | near Jupiter that night. But the following night, the starlets were still
184 | near Jupiter and still in a straight line. The next night, they were nearby
198 | and in a straight line again. By the fifth night, he hypothesized that the
212 | starlets were completing revolutions around Jupiter just as our own
222 | moon revolves around the earth. Galileo did not yet call these starlets
234 | "moons." Instead, he called them "wanderers." **(#2)**

240 | Galileo carried out his investigation with great care. He observed
250 | Jupiter and its wanderers every night for two months. Each night, he
262 | made drawings of the exact positions of Jupiter's companions. He
272 | recorded each starlet's position on the right or the left and closer or
285 | farther away from Jupiter. Galileo also noted that he could see no other
298 | stars for a long way on either side of Jupiter. One night, he noticed a
313 | fourth starlet near Jupiter. In addition, he documented that on some
324 | nights, one or two wanderers had disappeared. He concluded that the
335 | missing starlets were behind Jupiter. **(#3)**

340 | By the end of the two months, Galileo had plenty of data to confirm
354 | that the starlets were the four largest moons that orbit Jupiter. Today
366 | we call them the "Galilean moons." We now know that Jupiter has
378 | many more moons as well. **(#4)**

383 392 403 414 424 434 446 450	Did you notice Galileo's questions, his methodical search for answers, and the support for his conclusion? Did you ever observe something puzzling and ask, "What's that?" or "How does that work?" Your curiosity and your questions were the beginnings of doing science. If you then formulated a hypothesis, made some observations, and recorded what you found, you were doing what Galileo did and what scientists do today. **(#5)**

ACTIVITY L: **Rate Development**

Cold Timing [ ]   **Practice 1** [ ]

Practice 2 [ ]   **Hot Timing** [ ]

ACTIVITY A: **Vowel Combinations Review**

1	ee	ow	ir	oy	ay	or
2	au	ou	oo	i - e	oi	o - e
3	oa	er	ur	ea	ai	ar

ACTIVITY B: **Vowel Conversions Review**

i	e	a	o	u

ACTIVITY C: **Prefixes and Suffixes Review**

Prefixes

1	ad	im	be	com	de
2	con	per	dis	ab	pro

Suffixes

3	cious	al	ity	ence	y
4	or	ible	age	ture	ful
5	ary	cive	le	tious	ent

ACTIVITY D: Guided Strategy Practice

1	considerable	disappointment
2	reliability	professionally
3	tenacious	disorganization
4	dramatically	enlightenment

ACTIVITY E: Unguided Strategy Practice

1	honesty	inspirational
2	incorrectly	establishment
3	forgetfulness	inconsiderate
4	contribution	unconventional
5	traditionally	impressionable

ACTIVITY F: Spelling Dictation

1		**3**	
2		**4**	

ACTIVITY G: Meanings of Prefixes and Suffixes

ly indicates an **adverb**
ly = *in a manner that is*

a (Activity D) an **adverb** that means **in a manner that is professional**; doing a job the way a specially trained person would do

_____

b (Activity E) an **adverb** that means **in a manner that is incorrect**; doing something in a way that is not correct

_____

c (Activity E) an **adverb** that means **in a manner that is traditional**; doing something the way it has always been done

_____

ACTIVITY H: Word Reading Review

1 destructive   instrumentalist

2 reflective   inventiveness

3 incredible   communication

4 intolerable   indescribable

5 cultivate   administrative

ACTIVITY I: Sentence Reading

1. Harper is complaining that her boss is inconsiderate of her.

2. He was not only disrespectful but also unpredictable and intolerant.

3. The comprehensive website showed students how to take positive actions collectively.

4. Many readers find Lamar's collection of poems to be inspirational.

5. The employer was suspicious that a worker had incorrectly connected the cables and caused the power outage.

6. Young children are impressionable; they often mimic what they observe on television.

7. Opera, as well as rap music, can be meaningful and inspirational.

8. You should be concerned if your dog has lost considerable weight and isn't as exuberant as usual.

9. Sometimes, the 18th century is called the Age of Enlightenment.

10. If a box jellyfish stings an unsuspecting surfer, his or her arm could swell dramatically.

11. Jason is very persistent. His tutor is pleased that Jason is <u>tenacious</u> with his reading, always trying to succeed.

12. Brandon made an excellent contribution to the organization, with his <u>combination</u> of confidence, honesty, and reliability.

List 1

* **1** culture   *n.*   A **culture** is the way of life of a group of people who share similar beliefs and customs.

2 custom   *n.*   A **custom** is an activity, a way of behaving, or an event that is usual for a particular group of people.

3 tradition   *n.*   A **tradition** is a custom or belief that has existed for a long time.

4 language   *n.*   **Language** is a system of communication, which consists of a set of sounds and written symbols used for talking and writing.

5 politics   *n.*   **Politics** has to do with the actions or activities associated with governing a country.

* **6** civilization   *n.*   A **civilization** is an advanced culture characterized by cities, an organized political system, art, religion, education, and a writing system.

7 diffuse   *v.*   When people **diffuse** knowledge, customs, or skills, they spread them around to people of other cultures.

List 2

1	agriculture	*n.*	**Agriculture** consists of farming and the methods that are used to raise and take care of crops and animals.
2	irrigate	*v.*	To **irrigate** land means to supply it with water in order to help crops grow.
* **3**	produce	*v.*	If you **produce** something, you make or create it.
4	trade	*n.*	A **trade** is the skilled practice of a practical occupation.
5	authoritarian	*adj.*	If a government is **authoritarian**, the people in the country have no say in choosing the ruler and must give absolute obedience to one person or to a small group of people. The citizens do not have individual freedoms.
6	democratic	*adj.*	If a government is **democratic**, the people in the country choose their ruler or rulers by voting for them in elections. The citizens have individual freedoms.
* **7**	unify	*v.*	If things or parts **unify**, they are brought together to form one thing.

What is Culture?

13	If you wake up to rock music, put on denim jeans, drink orange juice for breakfast, and speak English, those things are part of your
25	
38	culture. If you eat flat bread for breakfast, speak Arabic, and wear a long cotton robe to protect you from the hot sun, those things are part
52	of your culture.

If you wake up to rock music, put on denim jeans, drink orange
juice for breakfast, and speak English, those things are part of your
culture. If you eat flat bread for breakfast, speak Arabic, and wear a
long cotton robe to protect you from the hot sun, those things are part
of your culture.

When some people hear the word "culture," they think of priceless
paintings and classical symphonies. Culture, as used in geography,
is the way of life of a group of people who share similar beliefs and
customs. These people may speak the same language, follow the
same religion, and dress in a certain way. The culture of a people also
includes their government, their music and literature, and the ways
they make a living. **(#1)**

A colorfully dressed dancer in South Korea reflects certain customs
that are important to her. Many of her beliefs and customs have been
passed down from distant ancestors. All of us hold certain beliefs and
act certain ways because of what we've learned in our culture. What
things are important in your culture? **(#2)**

Some 4,000 to 5,000 years ago, at least four cultures arose in Asia
and Africa. One developed in China along a river called the Huang He.
Another developed near the Indus River in South Asia, a third between
the Tigris and Euphrates rivers in Southwest Asia, and a fourth along
the Nile River in North Africa.

All four river-valley cultures developed agriculture and ways of
irrigating or bringing water to the land. Why was irrigation important?
Farming produced more food than hunting and gathering, which
meant that larger populations could develop. People then learned
trades, built cities, and made laws. **(#3)**

The river-valley cultures eventually became civilizations, which are
highly developed cultures. These civilizations spread their knowledge
and skills from one area to another, a process known as cultural
diffusion. **(#4)**

The kind of government, or political system, a society has reflects
its culture. Until a few hundred years ago, most countries had
authoritarian systems in which one person ruled with unlimited power.

Line numbers: 13, 25, 38, 52, 55, 66, 75, 90, 100, 114, 124, 128, 138, 151, 163, 175, 181, 194, 207, 219, 231, 237, 247, 258, 267, 276, 282, 291, 299, 311, 312, 323, 334

344	When the people of a country hold the powers of government, we
356	think of that government as a democracy. Citizens choose their leaders
367	by voting. Once in power, leaders in a democracy are expected to obey
380	a constitution or other longstanding traditions that require them to
390	respect individual freedoms. **(#5)**
393	Language is a powerful tool, offering a way for people to share
405	information. Sharing a language is one of the strongest unifying forces
416	for a culture. Languages spoken in a culture region often belong to the
429	same language family, or group of languages having similar beginnings.
439	Romance languages, for example, come from Latin, the language of
449	ancient Rome. Spanish, Portuguese, French, Italian, and Romanian are
458	in the Romance language family. **(#6)**
463	

ACTIVITY L: Rate Development

Cold Timing [   ]   Practice 1 [   ]

Practice 2 [   ]   Hot Timing [   ]

ACTIVITY A: Vowel Combinations Review

1	ou	er	oo	ur	oa	or
2	au	ea	ai	oy	ay	a - e
3	ee	ar	ow	e - e	oi	ir

ACTIVITY B: Vowel Conversions Review

o	i	u	a	e

ACTIVITY C: Prefixes and Suffixes Review

Prefixes

1	ad	com	a	mis	be
2	pre	pro	ab	im	un

Suffixes

3	tion	ist	ent	le	sion
4	ful	sive	ary	cial	ture
5	est	er	ity	tious	able

ACTIVITY D: Guided Strategy Practice

1 estimation   environmentally

2 correspondent   circumstantial

3 consistency   incorruptible

4 productivity   dissimilarity

ACTIVITY E: Unguided Strategy Practice

1 inference   misinformation

2 preventable   proportionate

3 extinction   incomprehensible

4 financial   excommunicate

5 evaluation   impracticality

ACTIVITY F: Spelling Dictation

1		3	
2		4	

ACTIVITY G: Meanings of Prefixes and Suffixes

a (Activity D) the state of being productive or getting a lot done

_____

b (Activity D) the quality of not being similar to another thing

_____

c (Activity E) not able to be comprehended because it's not easy to understand

_____

ACTIVITY H: Word Reading Review

1 tentatively   fundamentally

2 inconsiderate   impressionable

3 dramatically   professionally

4 confidence   disorganization

5 inspirational   communication

ACTIVITY I: Sentence Reading

1 For a lot of endangered species, extinction is still preventable.

2 While you are reading, you are constantly making inferences and drawing conclusions; you are making guesses about what the text doesn't tell you for sure.

3 Because of the inferences someone might make, the defendant's lawyer objected to the circumstantial evidence.

4 Historically, cultures tended to develop near rivers; sometimes, the cultures have grown to become civilizations.

5 Most occupations depend on organization, not disorganization.

6 Most people are counting on their storage systems for digital photos and music to be incorruptible.

7 The consumer organization evaluates products and puts the evaluations online.

8 Young children are impressionable, so they are vulnerable to feelings of rejection and disappointment.

9 When a church excommunicates someone, the church terminates his or her membership.

10 If you have poor grades because of forgetfulness and disorganization, establishment of new habits will help.

11 In spite of the financial <u>impracticality</u>, the city will build a new environmentally friendly library.

12 Many people believe that a crime should be punishable with a <u>proportionate</u> penalty; that is, a penalty that fits the size of the crime.

List 1

* **1** colony *n.* A **colony** is formed when people from a powerful country claim and occupy distant lands, even if other people already live there.

2 Portugal *n.* **Portugal** is a small country in Europe that is bordered by Spain.

3 Spain *n.* **Spain** is a country in Europe that borders Portugal and France.

4 France *n.* **France** is one of the largest countries in western Europe.

5 Great Britain *n.* **Great Britain** is one of the countries in the United Kingdom, an island in Europe.

* **6** foreign *adj.* Someone or something that is **foreign** comes from or relates to another country.

7 geography *n.* **Geography** is the study of countries of the world and of such things as the land, seas, climate, population, and towns or cities.

List 2

1. **territory**   *n.*   A **territory** is land that is under the control of an external government. Some **territories** are also colonies.

2. **inhabit**   *v.*   If a place or region is **inhabited** by a group of people or a species of animal, those people or animals live there.

3. **populate**   *v.*   If people or animals **populate** an area, those people or animals live there, often in large numbers.

* 4. **romanticize**   *v.*   When you **romanticize**, you think of something as better or more exciting than it really is.

* 5. **settle**   *v.*   When people **settle** a place or in a place, they start living there permanently.

6. **culture**   *n.*   A **culture** is the way of life of a group of people who share similar beliefs and customs.

7. **establish**   *v.*   If someone **establishes** an organization or system, he or she starts it or creates it.

Colonialism's Legacy

	Until the 1960s, a handful of countries ruled 85% of the globe.
12	Countries such as Portugal, Spain, France, and Great Britain governed
22	colonies on every continent (except Antarctica). This colonial period
31	lasted about 500 years, from the last part of the 15th century to the last
46	part of the 20th century. Today, only a small number of places on earth
60	are still listed as colonies, according to the United Nations. Most are
72	tiny islands. **(#1)**
74	A colony is a geographical area, territory, or country that is under
86	the political control of a foreign power. Typically, the parent or home
98	country colonized new land by sending people to explore or settle
109	there. This might have been a group of individuals who acted for the
122	government, such as the expedition of Christopher Columbus. Or, it
132	might have been a group of people that formed a company and asked
145	the government for permission to go. The Virginia Company of London
156	that landed on the shores of Virginia in 1607 is an example. **(#2)**
168	Many settlers romanticized the new life that awaited them overseas.
178	But when they arrived, they found they might have to fight for the land.
192	Some land was seemingly unpopulated. The remaining land was
201	pre-populated (people already lived there). The settlers fought the
210	original inhabitants for the land or forced them to move out of the
223	way. The colonists claimed the land because the parent country had
234	given them property rights. **(#3)**
238	Foreign countries established settlements in order to possess land
247	and gain wealth. So, they ordered their colonies to send resources
258	to them. These resources included lumber, furs, cotton, gold, silver,
268	coffee, and sugar. Parent countries also used colonies as markets for
279	their manufactured goods. These goods included textiles, furniture,
287	books, and tea, as well as tools, weapons, and countless other things
299	the colonists needed. **(#4)**

302	Ships carried the resources and goods back and forth. The home
313	country risked losing them to robbery or bad weather. Because of this
325	risk, merchant ships and war galleons would form a "treasure fleet"
336	and make the dangerous trip together. In 1622, one famous galleon,
347	the *Nuestra Señora de Atocha*, was on its way from Cuba to Spain,
360	carrying valuable resources from South America. But, it didn't make
370	it. Because of a hurricane, it crashed on the coral reefs and sank off
384	the coast of Florida. In 1985, a present-day treasure hunter, Mel Fisher,
397	began finding some of the *Atocha's* gold, silver, and emeralds. His
408	children still search for more of the *Atocha's* treasure today. **(#5)**
418	Colonialism has had a lasting influence on many countries that
428	once were colonies. The influence of colonialism might be seen in the
440	former colony's form of government, educational system, or culture,
449	including its language, religion, art, clothing, and cuisine. Colonialism
458	has also had a lasting influence on current events. As you encounter
470	today's news items, you might think about how you are seeing
481	reflections of colonialism. When people are fighting over land or other
492	possessions, perhaps the original inhabitants are trying to undo what
502	colonialism had done. Or, when you find out about the discovery of a
515	shipwreck, consider the possibility that ship was part of the larger set
527	of activities known as colonialism. **(#6)**
532	

ACTIVITY L: Rate Development

Cold Timing [ ]   Practice 1 [ ]

Practice 2 [ ]   Hot Timing [ ]

ACTIVITY A: Vowel Combinations Review

1 a - e |oo| oi ay ee au

2 ar o - e or i - e |ow| oy

3 ai |ea| u - e ou e - e oa

ACTIVITY B: Vowel Conversions Review

e o i a u

ACTIVITY C: Prefixes and Suffixes Review

Prefixes

1 re ab con im de

2 pro per dis com ad

Suffixes

3 le ence tial ance tious

4 al ism cial ary ly

5 cious able ible ic ate

ACTIVITY D: Guided Strategy Practice

1	graphical	indestructibility
2	significance	unimaginatively
3	deliberation	inconspicuous
4	repercussion	surreptitiously

ACTIVITY E: Unguided Strategy Practice

1	tremendously	indispensable
2	particularly	impressionistic
3	examination	unattractiveness
4	masterfully	inconsistently
5	capitalism	insurmountable

ACTIVITY F: Spelling Dictation

1		3	
2		4	

ACTIVITY G: Meanings of Prefixes and Suffixes

a (Activity D) the quality of not being able to be destroyed

_____

b (Activity D) in a manner that is not imaginative

_____

c (Activity E) in a manner that is not consistent or not in agreement

_____

ACTIVITY H: Word Reading Review

1 financial   misinformation

2 impracticality   environmentally

3 evaluation   circumstantial

4 incorruptible   incomprehensible

5 preventable   impressionable

ACTIVITY I: Sentence Reading

1. It is a wonderful victory to masterfully read long words.

2. Unfortunately, the family's debt rose to an insurmountable level during the recession.

3. Art that is impressionistic expresses an idea of something rather than showing the thing as we really see it.

4. For most professions, consistency and perseverance are good qualities to have.

5. Rather than rushing the patient examination, the emergency room doctor completed her task with deliberation.

6. Most corporations strive for effective organization and environmentally safe conditions.

7. Misinformation and attempts to foil communication were used to boost the movie's sinister plot.

8. The spectators did not realize the repercussions of their presence in the area; they were the ones who were delaying the rescue operations.

9. In my estimation, if a dog is your best friend, its name deserves your thought and imagination, but some dogs are unimaginatively named "Fido."

10. You can find all the baseball statistics you want (batting, pitching, fielding, attendance) on the graphical history of baseball website.

11. The children watched the performance from behind the curtains, trying to be <u>inconspicuous</u>.

12. Even though the instructor's methods were <u>unconventional</u>, they were tremendously effective; the results were fantastic.

List 1

1 frontier   *n.*   a. A **frontier** is the boundary between land that has been settled and land that has not been explored, developed, or settled.

                                   b. A **frontier** is the limit of knowledge or accomplishment in a field of knowledge beyond which there is more to explore, learn, and accomplish.

2 quest   *n.*   A **quest** is a search for something; it's often a long and difficult search.

* **3** accomplishment *n.*   An **accomplishment** is the successful completion of a task or the achievement of a goal.

4 miniature   *n.*   A **miniature** is something that is very small; often it's a smaller version of something that is normally much larger.

5 capsule   *n.*   A **capsule** is a small, closed container or compartment.

6 nanotechnology *n.*   **Nanotechnology** is the science of understanding and controlling things at the atomic level.

* **7** intrigues   *v.*   If something **intrigues** you, especially if it's something strange or unusual, that thing interests you and you want to know more about it.

List 2

1	boundary	*n.*	A **boundary** is an imaginary line that separates one area from other areas.
2	explore	*v.*	If you **explore** a place or an idea, you find out what it is like.
*** 3**	speculate	*v.*	If you **speculate** about something, you make guesses about its nature or about what might happen.
*** 4**	innovation	*n.*	An **innovation** is a new thing or a new method of doing something.
5	mantle	*n.*	In geology, the **mantle** is the part of the earth that lies between the crust and the core.
6	manipulate	*v.*	If you **manipulate** something that requires skill, such as a certain tool or a complicated piece of equipment, you move, operate, or control it.
7	maneuver	*v.*	If you **maneuver** something into or out of an awkward or unusual position, you skillfully move it there.

Frontiers of Tomorrow

9	The word *frontier* has traditionally meant the boundary between
22	land that has been settled and land that has not yet been explored,
33	developed, and settled. Today, people are more likely to use *frontier*
46	to mean the limit of knowledge or accomplishment in a field of study
57	beyond which there is more to explore, learn, and accomplish; for
66	example, *frontiers of medicine* or *frontiers of engineering*. Let's
74	examine a few of many 21st century frontiers. **(#1)**
82	Miniaturization is pushing the frontiers in manufacturing as
93	people take larger things (such as cameras) and make them smaller
103	and smaller. Miniaturization is also pushing the frontiers of physics,
113	chemistry, and biology. Humans are making things that have never
126	existed before. These things are so tiny that you cannot see them with
136	the unaided eye. We call this type of miniaturization *nanotechnology*.
147	Nanotechnology is helping us learn how atoms operate when you move
155	them around and build new structures with them. **(#2)**
164	In 1960, Richard Feynman, a famous scientist, speculated that
178	people should be able to make things as small as the cells in our
188	bodies. He also believed that you could maneuver things "atom
199	by atom." In 2005, a group of scientists accomplished both. By
209	manipulating atoms, they created the world's first nanocar—a car
220	about 20,000 times smaller than a human hair—visible through an
230	extremely powerful microscope that allowed the scientists to see the
232	wheels roll.
241	If scientists keep pushing the frontiers of miniaturization, whether
253	the products are visible or invisible, who knows how far these frontiers
266	will go? Perhaps we'll see a day when you would swallow a capsule
280	with a tiny video camera and a robot surgeon so that a doctor could
290	perform surgery that was previously impossible. Are parts of the
297	science fiction movie *Fantastic Voyage* becoming reality? **(#3)**
306	The frontiers of earth science are equally fascinating. Earth
316	scientists, people who explore the earth, are intrigued by what
329	they might find when they drill into the earth. In the 1960s, humans
340	successfully drilled into the crust, but no one has penetrated the
352	mantle, which makes up 84% of the Earth's volume. To reach the
365	mantle on land would mean drilling through the crust up to 37.3 miles.
376	Even if it were possible with the current equipment, drilling that
	far would take many, many years.

382	Now, scientists are considering three places in the ocean where
392	the crust is thin enough to attempt drilling 3.7 miles down to the
405	mantle. Even at one-tenth the distance compared to drilling on land,
417	this will still be a considerable challenge. After taking several years
428	to work on improving the equipment, the scientists hope to bring up
440	fresh samples of mantle material to study. Studying these samples
450	will lead to increased understanding of earthquakes, volcanoes, and
459	continents. How far will the frontiers of earth science advance during
470	your lifetime? **(#4)**
472	The frontiers of space exploration have fueled human imaginations
481	for centuries. People have written stories about space travel since
491	the 2nd century, when Lucian wrote the first known "science fiction."
502	Many centuries later, in the 1960s, humans completed numerous
511	journeys into space. On some of these journeys, astronauts made it
522	as far as the moon. Today, the goal is to send humans even farther.
536	Scientists talk of building space elevators, establishing space colonies,
545	and capturing asteroids. What will be the next frontier—Mars? **(#5)**
555	Humans are constantly advancing frontiers. Is it because humans
564	have a never-ending, insatiable quest for knowledge? Is it because of
576	the incentives for going deeper, traveling farther, and creating things
586	smaller than ever before? Or, is it because innovations make life easier
598	for humans? Whatever the reasons, you can participate in the exciting
609	future that lies before you. Perhaps you will contribute to exploring
620	one of these frontiers or even frontiers we can't yet imagine. **(#6)**
631	

ACTIVITY L: Rate Development

Cold Timing [ ]   **Practice 1** [ ]

Practice 2 [ ]   **Hot Timing** [ ]

Time for a Check-up!

Strategies for Reading Long Words

Overt Strategy

1. Circle the prefixes.
2. Circle the suffixes.
3. Underline the vowels.
4. Say the parts of the word.
5. Say the whole word.
6. Make it a real word.

EXAMPLE

reconstruction

Covert Strategy

1. Look for prefixes, suffixes, and vowels.
2. Say the parts of the word.
3. Say the whole word.
4. Make it a real word.

REWARDS®

REWARDS® Prefixes, Suffixes, and Vowel Sounds

Prefixes

Prefix	Key Word for Pronunciation	Meaning of Prefix	Prefix	Key Word for Pronunciation	Meaning of Prefix	Prefix	Key Word for Pronunciation	Meaning of Prefix
a	afraid	in, on; not; to	de	deforest	not, opposite of; away from	mis*	misprint	wrongly, wrong, not
ab	abnormal	away from; not, opposite of	dis*	disagree	not, opposite of	per	permit	through, throughout
ad	admit	to, toward; near, at	en	enlist	cause to; in, into; on	pre*	prepay	before
be	belong	to make; to provide with	ex	export	out of, away from	pro	proclaim	forward, before; instead of; in favor of
com	compare	together, with	im*	impossible	not, opposite of; in, into	re*	reprint	again, back
con	continue	together, with	in*	incomplete	not, opposite of; in, into	un*	unfair	not, opposite of

Suffixes

Suffix	Key Word for Pronunciation	Meaning of Suffix	Suffix	Key Word for Pronunciation	Meaning of Suffix	Suffix	Key Word for Pronunciation	Meaning of Suffix
able*	agreeable	able to be	est	greatest	the most	ment*	argument	act of, result of, state of
age	courage	act of, state of	ful*	careful	full of	ness*	kindness	state of, condition of
al	personal	like, related to	ible*	reversible	able to be	or*	inventor	person connected with
ance	disturbance	act of, state of, quality of	ic	classic	like, related to	ous*	nervous	full of
ant	informant	one who; inclined to	ing	running	doing something; related to	s	books	more than one; verb or adverb form
ary	missionary	related to; place for	ion*	opinion	act of, result of, state of	sion*	extension	act of, result of, state of
ate	operate	state of, quality of; to make	ish	vanish	like, related to	sive	expensive	act of, quality of
cial	special	like, related to	ism	realism	state of, action of	tial	partial	like, related to
cious*	precious	full of	ist	artist	person who does	tion*	action	act of, result of, state of
ed	landed	in the past; having	ity*	oddity	state of, quality of	tious*	cautious	full of
ence	occurrence	act of, state of, quality of	le	tackle	verb, adjective, or noun form	tive	attentive	act of, quality of
ent	consistent	one who; inclined to	less	useless	without, not	ture	picture	act of, result of, state of
er*	farmer	person connected with; more	ly*	safely	in a manner that is	y	thirsty	like; full of

Vowel Sounds

Vowel	Key Words	Vowel	Key Words	Vowel	Key Words
a	cat	ay	say	ow	low, down
e	let	ea	meat, thread	oy	boy
i	sit	ee	deep	ar	farm
o	hot	oa	boat	er	her
u	cup	oi	join	ir	bird
ai	rain	oo	moon, book	or	torn
au	sauce	ou	loud	ur	turn

Secondary

Spelling Words

Lesson 1

1. admit
2. misprint
3. abstract
4. display

Lesson 2

1. discard
2. commit
3. administer
4. absurd

Lesson 3

1. combine
2. misbehave
3. propose
4. conclude

Lesson 4

1. imperfect
2. reconstruct
3. unafraid
4. predict

Lesson 5

1. misinform
2. disagree
3. engrave
4. exclude

Lesson 6

1. unselfish
2. energetic
3. powerlessness
4. astonish

Spelling Words (continued)

Lesson 7

1. inspector
2. abnormal
3. ungrateful
4. astronomer

Lesson 8

1. intentional
2. comprehensive
3. distasteful
4. external

Lesson 9

1. perfectionist
2. precautionary
3. contaminate
4. incentive

Lesson 10

1. influence
2. informality
3. determination
4. entertainment

Lesson 11

1. continuous
2. substantial
3. gracious
4. reconsider

Lesson 12

1. impossible
2. uncomfortable
3. perseverance
4. unconventionality

Spelling Words (continued)

Lesson 13

1. expansion

2. performance

3. intensity

4. construction

Lesson 14

1. disagreement

2. adventure

3. reinvestigate

4. informative

Lesson 15

1. amendment

2. predictable

3. reflective

4. investigation

Lesson 16

1. completely

2. premature

3. immediately

4. reduction

Lesson 17

1. inventiveness

2. cautious

3. communication

4. instrumentalist

Lesson 18

1. forgetfulness

2. inconsiderate

3. honesty

4. establishment

Spelling Words (continued)

Lesson 19

1. preventable
2. financial
3. incomprehensible
4. productivity

Lesson 20

1. tremendously
2. insurmountable
3. significance
4. particularly

Meanings of Prefixes and Suffixes

Unit 1 Prefixes	Meanings introduced in:
dis = not, opposite of	Lesson 1
mis = wrongly, wrong, not	Lesson 1
in, im = in, into	Lesson 2
re = again, back	Lesson 3
pre = before	Lesson 3
un = not, opposite of	Lesson 4
in, im = not, opposite of	Lesson 4

Unit 2 Suffixes	Meanings introduced in:
ness indicates a *noun*; *ness* = state of, condition of	Lesson 6
ful indicates an *adjective*; *ful* = full of	Lesson 7
or or *er* indicates a *noun*; *or* or *er* = person connected with	Lesson 7

Unit 3 Suffixes	Meanings introduced in:
ion, *tion* or *sion* indicates a *noun*; *ion*, *tion* or *sion* = act of, result of, state of	Lesson 9
ment indicates a *noun*; *ment* = act of, result of, state of	Lesson 10

Unit 4 Suffixes	Meanings introduced in:
ity indicates a *noun*; *ity* = state of, quality of	Lesson 13
able or *ible* indicates an *adjective*; *able* or *ible* = able to be	Lesson 15

Unit 5 Suffixes	Meanings introduced in:
ous, *tious*, or *cious* indicates an *adjective*; *ous*, *tious*, or *cious* = full of	Lesson 17
ly indicates an *adverb*; *ly* = in a manner that is	Lesson 18

Vocabulary Log
Academic Vocabulary—Lessons 1–12

Lesson 1

1. **distract**—If someone or something **distracts** you, they take your attention away from what you are doing.
2. **admit**—If you **admit** that something bad or embarrassing is true, you agree, often unwillingly, that it is true.
3. **distraught**—If you are **distraught**, you are so upset and worried that you cannot think clearly.
4. **abstract**—**Abstract** ideas and **abstract** pieces of art are based on general ideas rather than specific people or things.

abstract

Lesson 2

1. **distinct**—If something is **distinct**, you can hear, see, or taste it clearly.
2. **absurd**—If you say that something is **absurd**, you are saying that it's ridiculous or that it doesn't make sense.
3. **discard**—If you **discard** something, you get rid of it because you no longer want it or need it.
4. **administers**—If someone **administers** something such as a country, business, or organization, he or she takes responsibility for organizing and supervising it.

absurd

Lesson 3

1. **betray**—If you **betray** someone who trusts you, you do something that hurts or disappoints that person.
2. **confine**—To **confine** someone or something to a particular place means to keep that person or thing from leaving or spreading beyond the place.
3. **respond**—When you **respond** to something that is done or said, you react to it by doing or saying something yourself.
4. **propose**—If you **propose** a plan or an idea, you suggest it.

propose

Academic Vocabulary (continued)

Lesson 4

1. **persist**—If you **persist** in doing something, you continue to do it, even though it is difficult or other people are against it.
2. **record**—If you **record** a piece of information or an event, you write it down, photograph it, or put it into a computer so that you or others can refer to it in the future.
3. **predict**—If you **predict** an event, you say ahead of time that it will happen.
4. **contrast**—If you **contrast** one thing with another, you show or tell about the differences between the two things.

record

Lesson 5

1. **exclude**—If you **exclude** someone from a place or activity, you prevent that person from entering the place or taking part in the activity.
2. **exceeds**—If something **exceeds** a particular amount, it is greater than, or more than, that amount.
3. **regret**—If you **regret** something that you have done, you wish that you had not done it, and, as a result, you feel sad or disappointed.
4. **comprehend**—If you cannot **comprehend** something, you cannot understand it.

exclude

Lesson 6

1. **astonishes**—If someone or something **astonishes** you, they surprise you very much.
2. **energetic**—An **energetic** person has a lot of energy. **Energetic** activities require a lot of energy.
3. **deliberate**—If something you do is **deliberate**, you decide ahead of time to do it.
4. **desperate**—If you are **desperate**, you are in a difficult situation and have little hope.

desperate

Academic Vocabulary (continued)

Lesson 7

1. **personal**—A **personal** opinion, quality, or thing belongs or relates to a particular person.
2. **exaggerates**—If someone **exaggerates**, he or she indicates that something is bigger, worse, or more important than it really is.
3. **abnormal**—Something that is **abnormal** is unusual, often in a way that is troublesome.
4. **abolish**—If someone in authority **abolishes** a practice, he or she puts an end to that practice.

exaggerates

Lesson 8

1. **intention**—An **intention** is an idea or plan of what you are going to do.
2. **explain**—If you **explain** something, you give details about it or describe it so that it can be understood.
3. **possess**—If you **possess** something, you have it or own it.
4. **external**—**External** means happening, coming from, or existing outside a place, person, or area.

explain

Lesson 9

1. **contaminated**—If something becomes **contaminated** by dirt, chemicals, or radiation, it becomes impure or harmful.
2. **incentive**—An **incentive** is something that encourages you to do something.
3. **immortal**—Someone or something that is **immortal** is famous and likely to be remembered for a long time.
4. **expedition**—An **expedition** is an organized journey made for a particular purpose, such as exploration.

contaminated

Academic Vocabulary (continued)

Lesson 10
1. **influence**—When people or things **influence** a person or situation, they have an effect on that person's behavior or that situation.
2. **dependent**—To be **dependent** on something or someone means to need that thing or person in order to succeed or survive.
3. **exuberant**—If you are **exuberant**, you are full of energy, excitement, and cheerfulness.
4. **determination**—**Determination** is the act of not letting anything stop you.

exuberant

Lesson 11
1. **substantial**—**Substantial** means large in amount or degree.
2. **strenuous**—A **strenuous** activity or action involves a lot of energy or effort.
3. **permanent**—**Permanent** means lasting forever or occurring all the time.
4. **gracious**—If someone is **gracious**, he or she is polite and considerate.

strenuous

Lesson 12
1. **legendary**—If you describe something or someone as **legendary**, you mean that they are very famous and that many stories are told about them.
2. **feature**—A **feature** of something is an interesting, important, or distinct part or characteristic of it.
3. **capable**—If you are **capable** of doing something, you are able to do it.
4. **persevere**—When you **persevere**, you keep on trying to do something even if it is hard.

persevere

Vocabulary Log
Content-Area Vocabulary—Lessons 13–20

Note: In Lessons 13-20, fourteen content-area words are taught in each lesson.
    Only four of those words per lesson are listed here.

Lesson 13

1. **organisms**—**Organisms** are plants or animals, including ones so small you cannot see them without using a microscope.
2. **resources**—**Resources** are things such as land, minerals, plants, and animals that people have available to them and can use to meet their needs.
3. **balance**—A **balance** is a situation in which all the parts are equal in strength or importance.
4. **appear**—If someone or something **appears**, they become visible or come into your sight.

organisms

Lesson 14

1. **scientific**—The word **scientific** is used to describe things that relate to science.
2. **process**—A **process** is a series of actions that have a particular result, such as factory workers taking raw materials and changing them into something else.
3. **alternatively**—We use the word **alternatively** to talk about something different from what has just been said.
4. **approximate**—If something is **approximate**, it is very close but not exactly the same as a certain number or a certain thing.

process

Lesson 15

1. **characteristic**—A **characteristic** is a feature or quality that is typical of a person, place, or thing.
2. **properties**—**Properties** are the characteristics or qualities that are typical of a place, an object, or a group of objects.
3. **abundant**—Something that is **abundant** is present in large quantities.
4. **determine**—To **determine** a fact means to discover it as a result of investigation.

abundant

Content-Area Vocabulary (continued)

Lesson 16

1. **emigrate**—If you **emigrate**, you leave your own country to live in another country.
2. **official**—If something is **official**, the government or someone in authority has approved it.
3. **develops**—When someone or something **develops**, they grow or change over a period of time and usually become more advanced, complete, or severe.
4. **contribute**—If you **contribute** to something, you say or do something to bring about a successful result.

contribute

Lesson 17

1. **curious**—When you are **curious**, you are eager to know or learn something.
2. **hypothesis**—A **hypothesis** is an idea that is suggested as a possible explanation for a particular situation or condition, but which has not yet been proved to be correct.
3. **observe**—If you **observe** a person or thing, you watch them carefully, especially in order to learn something about them.
4. **evidence**—**Evidence** is anything that makes you believe something is true or has really happened.

observe

Lesson 18

1. **culture**—A **culture** is the way of life of a group of people who share similar beliefs and customs.
2. **civilization**—A **civilization** is an advanced culture characterized by cities, an organized political system, art, religion, education, and a writing system.
3. **produce**—If you **produce** something, you make or create it.
4. **unify**—If things or parts **unify**, they are brought together to form one thing.

civilization

Content-Area Vocabulary (continued)

Lesson 19

1. **colony**—A **colony** is formed when people from a powerful country claim and occupy distant lands, even if other people already live there.
2. **foreign**—Someone or something that is **foreign** comes from or relates to another country.
3. **romanticize**—When you **romanticize**, you think of something as better or more exciting than it really is.
4. **settle**—When people **settle** a place or in a place, they start living there permanently.

settle

Lesson 20

1. **accomplishment**—An **accomplishment** is the successful completion of a task or the achievement of a goal.
2. **intrigues**—If something **intrigues** you, especially if it's something strange or unusual, that thing interests you and you want to know more about it.
3. **speculate**—If you **speculate** about something, you make guesses about its nature or about what might happen.
4. **innovation**—An **innovation** is a new thing or a new method of doing something.

accomplishment

Progress Monitoring Graph

Name: _____

Lesson

13	14	15	16	17	18	19	20

Number of Words Read Per Minute

220
215
210
205
200
195
190
185
180
175
170
165
160
155
150
145
140
135
130
125
120
115
110
105
100
95
90
85
80
75
70
65
60
55
50
45
40

Check-up Scores

Lesson 4		Lesson 8		Lesson 12		Lesson 16		Lesson 20	